Step

Lightly

In

Mind, body, spirit

Step Lightly In Mind, body, spirit

Cher Chevalier

Asherah Books
London

First published by Asherah Books, 2016

A CIP catalogue record for this book is available from the British Library.

ISBN 978-1-909187-88-7

CONTENTS

INTRODUCTION

I reveal in this book 10 simple *Step Lightly* steps that I follow to stay slim. I have been asked about my eating habits by hundreds of people over the years, so I have finally decided to share my steps with the world.

As well as my 10 steps, I have also included a *Step Lightly* Lifestyle and Meal Options section. All the foods and drinks listed herein are my favourites and are thus options only, not suggestions.

Many readers will already be familiar with the fact that I have been vegetarian since birth, as documented in my other books. I wish to add that the following 10 steps are my personal ones, based upon my experience and what has worked for me for all of my adult life. My selfie on the front cover of this book, which I took three months after my 44th birthday, shows that my steps have worked for me well into my 45th year (of this incarnation) and as such should continue to work for the rest of my life.

I am an Author and Spiritual Adviser, as many of you know. I am not a dietician, doctor, or nutritionist. I hope you will enjoy this very honest book.

Love and blessings, Cher x
www.spiritualadviser.co.uk

STEP 1
KNOW YOUR NOS

KNOW YOUR NOS

Knowing which foods and drinks that you need to say no to is vital. All of us are unique, and most of us have unique 'no' foods and drinks - or food intolerances if you will.

Many of us are familiar with the common allergy foods such as gluten, peanuts, wheat, and dairy, and everyone is now acutely aware of the effects that too much sugar has on the body. But our nos often consist of many surprising ingestible items. One of my no foods is cucumber!

Don't be fooled by foods and drinks that you crave - these could be nos for you too. If you are uncertain regarding your specific nos then simply *Step Lightly* and monitor how your body reacts after ingesting certain foods and drinks. You will soon be able to pin point those that suit you and the nos that don't.

I will share with you four examples of just how shocking some people's nos can be:

1. One of my close friends can tolerate milk but if she eats cheese, her face swells up like a full moon.
2. I know a young man who collapsed in the street after he ate a packet of energy sweets.
3. A client of mine cannot eat oranges or drink orange juice without coming out in blotches all over their body.
4. A lady I spoke with at a charity event refused the wine offered as she had only ever sipped wine once and had fainted. She can however drink spirits.

Make a list of all of your nos and be sure to avoid having them on a regular basis. Or if needs be, completely eliminate them altogether.

I have created a page for you overleaf to make your own *Step Lightly* list of nos.

STEP LIGHTLY
NOS LIST

STEP 2
IT TAKES TWO

IT TAKES TWO

According to my steps, it takes two full meal options per day, along with a *Step Lightly* third option, for me to stay slim.

Simply put:

If I have a *Step Lightly* breakfast option, then I will also have a full lunch option and a full dinner option.

If I have a full breakfast option, then I will also have a *Step Lightly* lunch option and a full dinner option.

I always have a daily full dinner option. And only switch between the breakfast and lunch *Step Lightly* options. If this rule is not adhered to, I tend to lose weight. Keeping to my routine of 'it takes two' full meal options daily, along with a *Step Lightly* third option for breakfast or lunch, has ensured that since my late teens, I have always weighed between 48 and 50 kilos, which is right for me and my build.

Desserts are optional too and I may have one if I so desire on any given day. I have included *Step Lightly* dessert options as well as 'twice weekly' full dessert options in the Dessert Options section.

STEP 3
TEST YOUR TASTEBUDS

TEST YOUR TASTEBUDS

Enjoying food that both tastes delicious and is good for you is one of the great pleasures in life. It is estimated that people spend up to a third of their lives eating, cooking, and dining with friends and family. This does not include the amount of time the average person thinks about food. And with so much of our precious time being spent in this way, surely we should aim to do our best to enjoy it fully.

There are thousands of foods and flavours to sample from the numerous cuisines around the world, so test your tastebuds, experiment and enjoy! But *Step Lightly,* both with your tastebuds and your intuition.

When trying new foods and flavours, test a tiny amount - testing not only the tastes, but the smells, as well as the look of the foods, and how you feel about them intuitively. If you sense they are not for you, they may not be. Move on and continue discovering all of the wonderful ones that are right for you.

Here is a list of more than a hundred of my favourite natural foods:

Blackberries, Raspberries, Sultanas, Blueberries, Gooseberries, Acai Berries, Elderberries, Goji Berries, Watermelons, Red Grapes, Avocados, Raisins, Blackcurrants, Cranberries, Pink Grapefruit, Pumpkins, Cantaloupe Melons, Honey Dew Melons, Dates, Green Grapes, Noni Fruit, Guavas, Prunes, Lychees, Apples, Mandarin Oranges, Kiwis, Cherries, Nectarines, Apricots, Mangoes, Olives, Custard Apples, Coconuts, Dragon Fruit, Oranges, Pears, Plums,

Star Fruit, Kumquats, Black Cherries, Lemons, Passion Fruit, Mangosteen Fruit, Pomegranates, Figs, Satsumas, Peaches, Bananas, Mint, Elderflower, Vanilla, Basil, Chives, Oregano, Parsley, Sage, Garlic, Okra, Alfalfa, Purslane, Cauliflowers, Brussels Sprouts, Broccoli, Aubergines, Beans, Petit Pois Peas, Iceberg Lettuce, Green Cabbages, Curly Kale, Garden Peas, Green Peppers, Butter Beans, Sweet Corn, Chicory, Bok Choy, Water Cress, Celeriac, Spinach, Runner Beans, Courgettes, Baby Corn, Artichokes, Chard, Water Chestnut, Rocket, Sugar Snap Peas, Kale, Onions, Chickpeas, Cress, Mushrooms, Celery, Lentils, White Cabbage, Leek, Yam, Asparagus, Potatoes, Sweet Potatoes, Radishes, Parsnips, Turnips, Carrots, Beetroot, Swede, Cashews, Almonds.

STEP 4
BLESS THE BELLY

BLESS THE BELLY

Step Lightly and bless the belly that you have been blessed with, after all it is the only one you have, and it needs to last you for your entire incarnation. It is estimated that the approximate size of an adult human stomach is that of a fist.

One bowlful, or one plateful for each meal is enough. Any more than that and you will overload your system. Not only that, but regular overeating can cause the stomach to stretch, resulting in a need for you to eat more and more to feel full.

Special occasions may find a lot of us over-indulging, which as a treat should be okay. But by special occasions I mean a birthday party, wedding, or Christmas, not weekly and most certainly not daily events.

The human intestine - the long tube that runs from the stomach to the anus - is approximately 20 feet long, and only one inch in diameter. Everything you consume travels through this delicate channel. Keep this in mind to avoid overeating. Keep your belly blessed!

STEP 5
SNACK SAVVY

SNACK SAVVY

Step Lightly with your snacks between meals. Snacks, I believe are important, so long as they are healthy.

I have listed just a few of my favourite healthy snacks that I can enjoy any time of day. These types of snacks I often take with me in my bag when I am travelling too:

Ready Salted Crisps
Kale Chips
Almonds
Rice Crackers
Pumpkin Seeds
Cashew Nuts
Celery
Banana
Red Apple
Watermelon
Pomegranate Seeds

STEP 6
SWEET SAVVY

SWEET SAVVY

Step Lightly on sweet street. All of us have our favourite sweets and treats, and it's good to enjoy them from time to time. I personally don't feel it's good or necessary for me to have my favoured sweets and treats on a regular basis though.

Sugar, I feel should be had in moderation only. I don't have sugar in my drinks, or on my cereals. I don't add sugar to anything that I eat or drink!

I have listed a few of my favourite sweets and treats that I enjoy only on occasion. And when I do, it is in small amounts. For example:

Dark Mint Chocolate (three pieces maximum - never a whole bar)
Apple Crumble and Vegan Cream (a small slice)
Almond Flapjack (one piece)
Peanut Butter and Coconut Energy Balls (three small ones)
Vanilla Vegan Ice-Cream (two small scoops)
Mango Sorbet (two small scoops)
Salted Caramel Cupcake (one small one)
Strawberry Liquorice (three bite size pieces)

STEP 7
SUP SAVVY

SUP SAVVY

Step Lightly when supping sugary or alcoholic drinks. On the whole, I tend to keep to clear drinks, and ones with the least sugar. I drink still water all day, every day.

When I do have alcoholic drinks, I keep to a maximum of two drinks for the entire evening, or a maximum of three drinks if it's my birthday or Christmas.

I have listed my favourites:

Step Lightly Non-Alcoholic Drinks

Still Water
Sparkling Water
Soda Water
Hemp Milk (natural omega 3)
Coconut Milk
Herbal Tea
Fresh Mint Tea

Step Lightly Alcoholic Drinks

Vodka and Sparkling Water
Gin and Soda
Bacardi and Soda
Champagne
Elderflower Martini
Rose Petal Martini

STEP 8
PRACTICE PEACE

PRACTICE PEACE

Step Lightly and practice peace. Stress triggers many negatives: anxiety, anger, food cravings, dis-ease, and health problems. Peace has a good effect on your mind, body, spirit and health.

Choose to be peaceful. Don't allow anyone - including you - to steal your peace. Create it, build it, keep it, for you to enjoy and share with others.

When things disturb you, train yourself to react peacefully - make a habit of it until your natural response is one of peace.

I have included a list of ways for you to practice peace:

Relax; rest every part of your body
Quieten your mind until there are no thoughts
Meditate on peace
Pray for inner peace
Read
Don't compare yourself with others; there's only one of you and you're it
Love and forgive yourself
Be compassionate with yourself and others
Breathe slowly and deeply until calm on the inside
Be patient with yourself and others
Be non-violent in your thoughts, words and actions
Make your home your haven of peace and tranquility
Be silent and still on purpose, without talking or thinking; just be.

STEP 9
HAPPINESS HEALS

HAPPINESS HEALS

Step Lightly on your very own pleasure trip and discover all the things that make you happy. Be thorough and uncover the myriad yet-to-find wonders that will lift your spirits.

Be content by acknowledging all the good in your life and in the world around you. Be joyful and be around those that bring you joy.

Happiness heals us in heart, mind, body and soul. Cheerfully and with a positive plan, begin your search for eternal happiness.

I have included a list of just a few of the things that make me happy:

Singing - at times certain songs, but mostly from the heart - out loud
Dancing - often alone and in my pyjamas
Laughing
Smiling
Blessing others when they least expect it
Going to Comedy Clubs
Walking in beautiful places
Watching funny movies
Exercising - yoga and exercise bike
Playing with my pets
Studying wildlife
Writing books, poems and songs - especially amusing ones for children
Dining with friends and family

Learning fascinating facts about nature
Seeing my students achieve success
Pondering the wonders of invisible forces
Exploring esoteric secrets revealed by The Divine
Focusing on my love for God

STEP 10
LOVE & LET LIVE

LOVE & LET LIVE

Step Lightly on this planet. Care for yourself and others. Eat a harmless diet. Live kindly and karma-free.

We sentient Beings are all travelling through this world together, visiting this earth temporarily, be it for a nanosecond or a century. Let us all gently *Step Lightly* and all enjoy the journey, causing harm to none.

All Beings wish for the same fundamental things: to be free, happy, safe, secure, fed, and watered. I believe that most if not all of us Beings wish to be loved too. In unity we can achieve this.

As human beings we have a duty of care over other Beings on earth. We have a responsibility to ensure that all Beings in our world have their fundamental needs met. We have every right to care and protect. We have no right to kill any Being. Dying is a natural process of life, killing is not.

As a sentient Being myself (having the ability to suffer) I do not wish to be murdered and eaten for food. Feeling this way about myself, it stands to reason thus that I do not wish for any other sentient Being to be murdered and eaten for food. Hence my choice to retain a lifestyle without eating meat or fish. I was born to vegetarian parents, and have chosen to adhere to their views of a non-violent diet for the whole of my life.

You too have the capacity to choose what is right and good. Be your very best self. Other Beings have the same right to live as you. They are counting on you!

STEP LIGHTLY
LIFESTYLE

INTRODUCTION

As a Spiritual Adviser I suggest to clients and my students alike that to have a *Step Lightly* lifestyle involves living a good life, which requires practical application. It is not enough to merely read about, think about, or even discuss living a good life: one must apply techniques to ensure positive transformational results!

The following techniques, if applied with pure motives, could change one's life simply yet dramatically, for the betterment of all. Be always mindful that you as a Being have power, and that everything that you eat, drink, think, do and say will either add to the light within you and thus in the world around you, or add to the darkness within you and thus in the world around you.

I wish you well on your *Step Lightly* journey! May The Divine guide you.

STEP LIGHTLY
THOUGHTS

Step Lightly in your thoughts. Choosing to have good thoughts is a powerful step. I emphasise the word choosing, for the simple reason that your thoughts are your own: you should be able (with some effort) to choose which type of thoughts you allow in your mind.

Be in charge! If you do not like the thought patterns that have crystallised in your mind over time - if they are not good and positive - choose not to allow them any more.

Here is a technique: as a negative thought arises within your thought field, stop it immediately. Don't allow it to run into a chain of thoughts. Stop it at the first negative thought.

And, if necessary, say to yourself inwardly, or aloud if you wish, "I choose to have good, positive, productive, happy thoughts." Just as you would not allow rubbish to keep flying into your home, do not allow negative thinking to invade your inner home!

STEP LIGHTLY
SPEECH

Step Lightly in your speech; so much so that if what you have to say is not true, necessary and kind, you will not say it! Words have power. And just as thoughts crystallise and manifest over time, so do words.

I have chosen to do my best to not use swear words, for the simple reason that their root is to cause offence. I have also chosen to do my best to not tell lies, but instead to tell the truth. Gossiping is another misuse of speech that I have chosen to avoid, as it is negative and causes harm.

Be sure that your words do not humiliate others. If you have a grievance to address with someone, speak truthfully, calmly, and say only what is necessary. Make your words edifying, not derogatory. Remember that your words will either create light or add to the darkness.

Ultimately, speak only if your words will have more of a positive or correctional impact than your silence!

STEP LIGHTLY
ACTIONS

As you learn to empower yourself with the *Step Lightly* in Thought and Speech techniques above, you should find it much easier, and indeed more natural, for your actions to become harmless. Violence is the lowest form of communication, meaning that one has so little Mastery over oneself and one's emotions, that one has to resort to the lowest negative impulse – an act of violence.

If you feel rage rising from within, do not act on it, just watch and observe it. If possible, step into the fresh air, put on some music, or even better watch or look at something funny!

Within moments, rage dissipates if it is not acted upon. The more you practice this technique, the more peace and joy you will create in your life.

STEP LIGHTLY
MEDITATION

Step Lightly in meditation. Go within to find your inner sanctuary inside of your heart. Meditation is a key to overcoming your lower self - made up of negative emotions, anxiety and fear.

You must seek this inner sanctuary, peacefully. Train the mind to be silent at your command. Immerse yourself in the inner bliss that resides in your heart centre as the powerful, loving you.

Whether you prefer to meditate to music or in silence, or even chanting, do so with the intention of finding The Divine within you.

I have created a page for you overleaf to make your own *Step Lightly* list of meditation experiences.

STEP LIGHTLY
MEDITATION EXPERIENCES

STEP LIGHTLY
KINDNESS

Step Lightly and kindly - kindness is a strength, not a weakness. Being kind means that you are thinking, speaking, acting and living for the betterment of all Beings. Not just humans, and not just yourself.

Discipline is a close cousin of kindness. If you are not being disciplined with yourself, or your loved ones, you are not really being kind.

Positive, good and structured discipline is a prerequisite for living a good life. If you mistake kindness for weakness and overindulge yourself or your loved ones, emotionally or otherwise, you won't be contributing to the evolutionary process. And thus not benefitting the Being in question.

Compassion is a close friend of kindness. Being compassionate means that you are willing to go the extra mile and even suffer for the sake of others. If we were all compassionate to all Beings there would be very little suffering in the world.

Look for opportunities to show compassion and kindness!

STEP LIGHTLY
KARMA

Step Lightly enough to balance your karma and become karma-free. Balancing one's karma is one of the main reasons for being on earth. So before you leave this dimension, be sure that you have done everything to clear your karmic debt. If you owe someone something, settle it, be it money, time, or an apology. Tie up loose ends. Don't leave your tail behind you. Be practical.

Anyone can be taken from this life at any time: it is not just the elderly and the unwell who should live this way. The most spiritual way to live is to be happy, helpful, and karma-free, so that you are ready to meet your Divine Creator in any given moment - be it via Mystical attunement, or by dying and leaving this world!

STEP LIGHTLY
GIVING

As part of living a *Step Lightly* life, giving is paramount. It need not always be money; it may be your time, clothes or your advice. Try and be mindful of opportunities to give. Be helpful. Small things can count in big ways.

Remember that every breath you take is a gift given to you; it is not yours. If it were yours, you wouldn't need to rely on the air to breathe!

I encourage my students to give to others, especially to the needy and vulnerable, in a variety of ways. Give, and see how happy it makes you.

Look for opportunities to be giving!

STEP LIGHTLY
CO-CREATOR

As co-creators with The Divine Creator we are destined to aim for the very highest and to achieve what some may call miracles!

Step Lightly and search deep inside you to discover what moves you. Every Being is completely unique and bestowed with gifts by The Divine Creator. Find out what your gifts are by searching within your heart, soul and mind:

What bothers you most about this world?

What makes you most happy?

What would you change about the world right now, if you could?

Focus on the three questions. And when the energy emerges to spur you on, aim with all your might to fulfil your destiny. You may invent the next top tech gadget. You may discover the next breakthrough in medicine. You may even save the planet from environmental disaster. There are no limits!

STEP LIGHTLY
GRATITUDE

Step Lightly and in gratitude as you tread your path. This life can be beset with tests, trials, and a multitude of contradictions. Yet every one of them is an opportunity to not only learn from, but to become empowered by.

It may be tough at times, but we will get there, and reach great lofty heights with a gratitude attitude - if we remind ourselves that we are continually evolving.

As we gain in wisdom and grow in knowledge we become less subject to the powers of fate and more in command of our destiny!

Write a gratitude list. Include everything and everyone that you are grateful for.

I have included a page for you overleaf to write your own *Step Lightly* gratitude list.

STEP LIGHTLY
GRATITUDE LIST

STEP LIGHTLY
FORGIVENESS

Step Lightly and write two very detailed forgiveness lists:

Step Lightly Forgiveness List 1 - include everyone that you need to forgive, for everything, no matter what. Along with what you are forgiving them for.

Step Lightly Forgiveness List 2 - include everything that you need to ask your Divine Creator to forgive you for, include everything, no matter what, and no matter how small you may deem the thing to be.

Write abbreviations or use initials and symbols on your lists if you are concerned about privacy. No one else need ever understand or indeed even ever see your two *Step Lightly* Forgiveness Lists.

As you begin these important works, pay attention to your inner prompts, your conscience, and respond accordingly. You may feel the need to actively apologise to someone in person, or even go so far as to send a gift to heal a rift.

Ultimately, you could feel so inspired by the healing your lists bring, that you may even choose to do something for God.

I have created two *Step Lightly* forgiveness list pages for you overleaf to get you started.

STEP LIGHTLY
FORGIVENESS LIST 1

STEP LIGHTLY
FORGIVENESS LIST 2

STEP LIGHTLY
PRAYER

Step Lightly, gently and quietly. Get comfortable. Be still in mind, body and spirit. No wriggling or fidgeting. Be silent in mind, body and spirit. No thinking or questioning.

Once immersed in your inner silence, breathing deeply, with eyes closed, use your inner eye and seek the light within you!

When the light emerges from your spirit, revealing itself to you inwardly, without doubt, and with faith, asking for nothing - pray to enter into The Divine Presence.

In this blissful state of prayer, all the petitions you wish to be made known to God are imparted by your spirit.

Be patient. Sit and wait. God may speak to your heart or spirit in response. God is all-knowing and all-powerful. Nothing is impossible with God.

Praying in this way will help you to establish a relationship with God. Honour your prayer time. It is sacred.

I have created a page for you overleaf to make your own list of *Step Lightly* prayer experiences.

STEP LIGHTLY
PRAYER EXPERIENCES

STEP LIGHTLY
FOREVER

You are you forever!

Your every thought, choice, word and deed is co-creating your very existence and the circumstances within it. Imagine how excellent your existence can become by you realising your power right now, and the interconnected impact it is to have on your future - be it in this lifetime or the next.

As incarnated Beings we are all 'tourists' in this physical dimension. Once fully aware of this reality, one becomes so humbled that selfish abuse of others, be they human, animal or the earth itself, becomes impossible.

We are all responsible for our own 'roles' in 'life'. Would you feel ready to meet your God if today were your last day on earth, and stand boldly as the co-creator that The Divine willed for you to be? If not, then there is work for you to do on you.

Step Lightly in all the ways mentioned and more, and become happy and karma-free in mind, body and spirit, feeding the body spiritual (harmless) foods, living as the divine eternal you, forever!

MEAL OPTIONS

INTRODUCTION

As mentioned earlier in Step 2 - It Takes Two: I choose to eat two full meal options per day, along with a *Step Lightly* third option - either for breakfast or lunch - for me to stay slim. Simply put:

On a day that I choose a *Step Lightly* breakfast option, then I will also have a full lunch option and a full dinner option.

On a day that I choose to have a full breakfast option, then I will also have a *Step Lightly* lunch option and a full dinner option.

The options listed in the following pages are just some of the many meals I favour and choose to include in my daily mix-and-match *Step Lightly* and full meal options.

My body, I believe, is to some degree a combination of a machine and a creature, thus fully trainable. The steps and meal options that I follow allow me to enjoy a vast variety of foods and flavours from a multitude of cuisines, and ensures that I never need diet or feel hungry. And I stay slim!

I have created pages throughout this section for you to create your own *Step Lightly* and full meal options.

BREAKFAST OPTIONS

STEP LIGHTLY OPTIONS

Granola with Raisins and Hemp Milk

Mixed Melon and Pomegranate Seeds

Banana and Strawberry Smoothie

FULL OPTIONS

Avocado and Chilli on Double Wholemeal Toast

Vegan Sausage, Hash Browns, Baked Beans,
Mushrooms and Tomatoes

Pancakes with Maple Syrup and Blueberries

STEP LIGHTLY
BREAKFAST IDEAS

STEP LIGHTLY OPTIONS

FULL OPTIONS

LUNCH OPTIONS

STEP LIGHTLY OPTIONS

Vegetable Soup - Onions, Carrots, Courgettes, Potatoes,
Thyme, Salt and Pepper

Chickpea and Rocket Salad with Apple Cider Vinegar,
Balsamic, and Olive Oil Dressing

Lentil and Spinach Dahl

FULL OPTIONS

Vegan Burger in a Bun with Lettuce and Tomato Ketchup

Asian Vegetable Stir-Fry with Avocado Sushi Rolls

Marinated Tofu with Rice and Green Beans

STEP LIGHTLY
LUNCH IDEAS

STEP LIGHTLY OPTIONS

FULL OPTIONS

DINNER OPTIONS

FULL OPTIONS

Roast Dinner - Vegan Beef, Roast Potatoes, Yorkshire Pudding, Sage and Onion Stuffing, Broccoli, Carrots, Onion Gravy

Spaghetti Bolognese with Vegan Mince

Coconut Curry and Basmati Rice with Vegan Chicken Pieces

Tofu Pad Thai and Vegetable Spring Rolls

Vegetable Stew with Dumplings

Asparagus and Baby Squash Risotto with Crispy Sage

Sweet Potato Pie with Mash and Sugar Snap Peas

STEP LIGHTLY
DINNER IDEAS

STEP LIGHTLY OPTIONS

FULL OPTIONS

DESSERT OPTIONS

STEP LIGHTLY DAILY OPTIONS

Mango Sorbet

Fruit Salad

Coconut Yogurt

TWICE WEEKLY FULL OPTIONS

Apple Crumble with Vegan Vanilla Ice-Cream

Chocolate Brownie with Vegan Chocolate Sauce

Salted Caramel Vegan Cheesecake

STEP LIGHTLY
DESSERT IDEAS

STEP LIGHTLY OPTIONS

FULL OPTIONS

STEP LIGHTLY
NOTES

STEP LIGHTLY
NOTES

STEP LIGHTLY
NOTES

Printed in Great Britain
by Amazon

80367194R00071